Tilak saw a robin.

1

Mo saw a cat.

She shouted, 'Scat, cat!' and
the cat ran away.

3

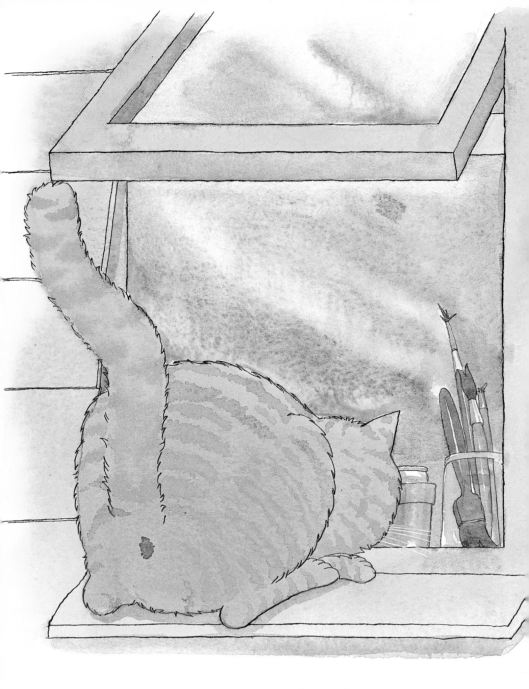

Then the cat came back.

Tilak shouted, 'Scat, cat!' and
the cat ran away.

But it came back
with another cat!

Mo put a bucket against the door.

Then she made a notice.

ealand
ples

Tilak made a big dog.

His dog said, 'Grr!'

The cats ran away and
they didn't come back.

Tilak and Mo looked at the nest.

They looked at the nest every day.

They saw a father robin and a mother robin.

Then they saw the baby robins.

They gave the dog a medal.